FAMILY ENTERTAINMENT NETWORK™

SONG BOOK

from the videos of

The Animated Stories
from the New Testament™
Series 1

Table of Contents

From the animated video - **A K**ING IS **B**ORN

A KING IS BORN

Lyrics by
CAROL LYNN PEARSON

Music by
LEX DE AZEVEDO

born of love. God's love a gift to all.

Bow ev'-ry knee, ev'-ry tongue tell the sto-ry:_____ To - night a King is

born.

Gen - tly a

King is born. To - night a King is

born. Born of in-no-cence, born of love; God's love, a

gift to all. Bow ev'-ry knee, ev'-ry tongue tell the sto-ry:_____ To-

night a King is born. To-night_____ a King_____ is

born._____

The Making of Animation

The scripts are outlined and written in accordance with the scriptures.

Richard Rich gives direction to artists as they create the storyboards.

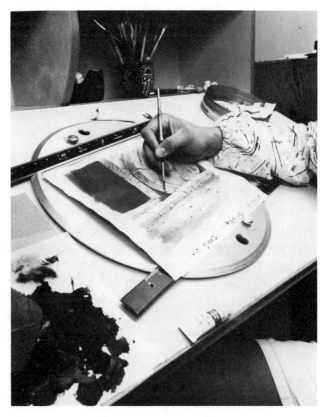

Artists design the many background scenes used in each animation.

From the animated video - **JOHN THE BAPTIST**

PREPARE YE THE WAY

Lyrics by
CAROL LYNN PEARSON

Music by
LEX DE AZEVEDO

Pre-

pare— ye the way— of the Lord. Pre - pare— ye the way— for His
pare— ye the way— of the Lord. De - clare— ye the day— of His
pare— ye the way— of the Lord. Oh, share— the good news— of His

king - dom. His path— we must clear,— for the time is— here to pre-
com - ing. Our voic - es we'll raise,— as we sing His— praise. Oh, pre
gos - pel. The day— is at hand;— let the faith - ful— stand, and pre

Watch,____ for the Lord comes to-mor-row! Pre

pare the way of the Lord.

Love__ one an-oth-er, the proph-ets said. Bear__ one an-oth-er's

*From the animated video - **THE PRODIGAL SON***

WELCOME HOME

Lyrics by
CAROL LYNN PEARSON

Music by
LEX DE AZEVEDO

home, wel-come home, wel-come home. You've come back to the light;__ wel-come

home. We'll dance through__ the night; wel-come home There's__

joy in our hearts;__ let the ce-le-bra-tion start. Wel-come home, wel-come home, wel-come

home. Yes-ter-day__ has fad-ed, now it's in the__ past.__ The

home,   wel-come home,   wel-come   home.

To - ge - ther   ev - er - more.

From the animated video - **THE GOOD SAMARITAN**

MY HANDS

Lyrics by
CAROL LYNN PEARSON

Music by
LEX DE AZEVEDO

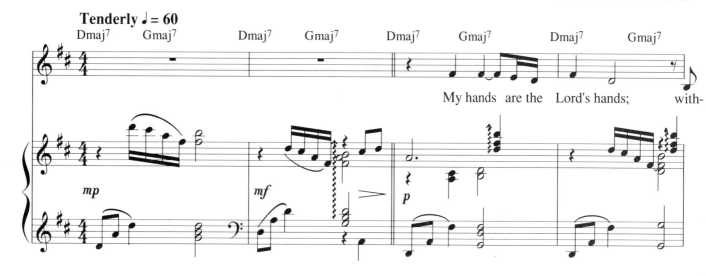

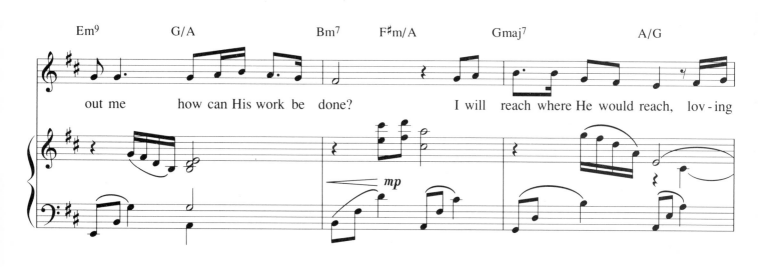

Help me, Lord, let me live so my neigh-bor will know that You are al-ways near.

Tempo Primo

My mouth is the Lord's mouth; with-out me how can His voice be heard? I will say what He would say, speak-ing love and life each day, and ev'-ry-one who's near will hear His word.

From the animated video - **THE MIRACLES OF JESUS**

THE MIRACLE OF LOVE

Lyrics by
CAROL LYNN PEARSON

Music by
LEX DE AZEVEDO

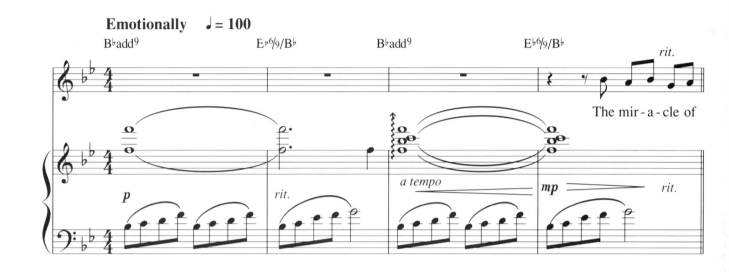

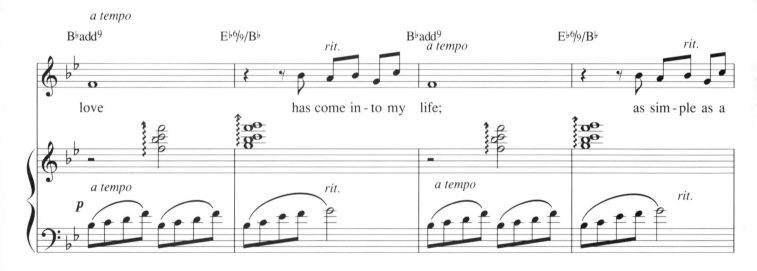

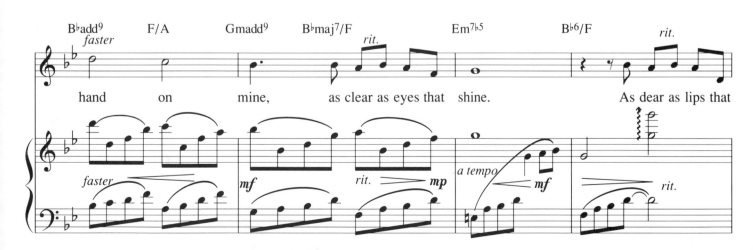

Tempo Primo

all day long and hum it while I'm sleep - ing.

My song is sweet thanks - giv - ing

that al - ways I'll be liv - ing, yes al - ways I'll be liv - ing

the mir - a - cle of love.

Director, Richard Rich, skillfully directs the actors and actresses used in the animations.

The voice of Mary is recorded.

The voice recordings are broken down letter by letter, frame by frame, by the track reader and timed for the animations.

The artists draw pencil sketches of each character.

From the animated video - **SAUL OF TARSUS**

HELP ME

Lyrics by
MARWENNA HAVER

Music by
LEX DE AZEVEDO

Am   Em/G   Fmaj⁹   Em/G   Am   Em/G

set out to drown___ me right from the start.___ Rag - ing storms have de - layed___ me, clouds have

Fmaj⁹   Dm⁷⁽♭⁵⁾/F   C/G   Dm/G   C/G   Am

shad - ed my heart. But the sun has re - flect - ed my faith in its rays, smil - ing

F   Dm⁷   Gsus   G   C   C/E

down as I fol - low His ways. Help me fight a good

F   C/E   Dm   Dm/F   Gsus   G   G/F

fight. Help me win with Thy might.

32

Help me fol-low the light. Help me, Lord,_____

to fight a good fight.

From the dis-tance I see____ the light

bec-kon-ing me____ to-ward e-ter-ni-ty____ And

34

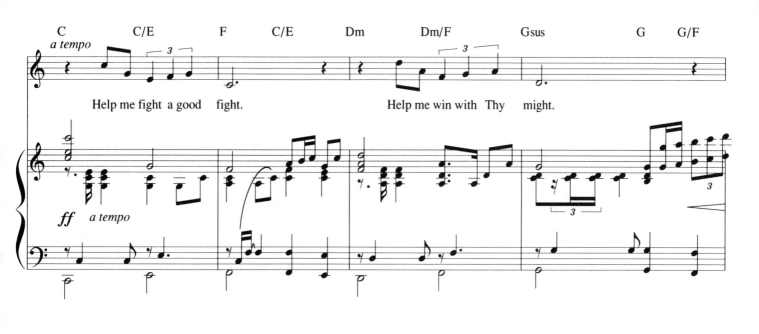

From the animated video - **HE IS RISEN**

HE GAVE HIS LIFE FOR ME

Lyrics by
JULIE DE AZEVEDO
and
LEX DE AZEVEDO

Music by
LEX DE AZEVEDO

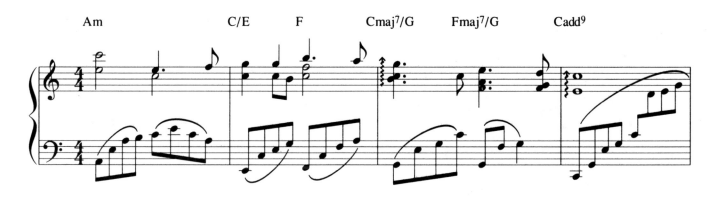

He showed His love for me. He led the

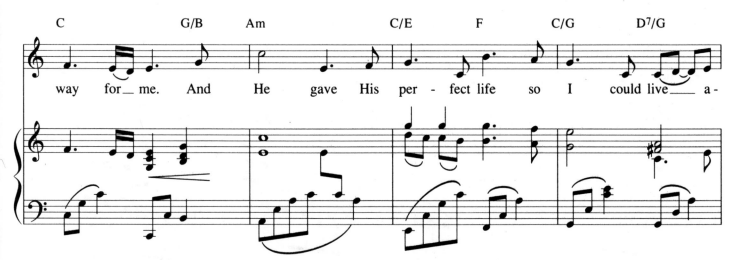

way for me. And He gave His per-fect life so I could live a-

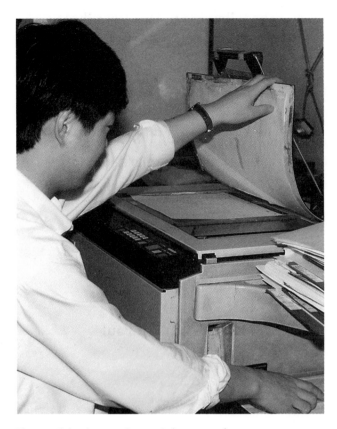

The pencil sketches are photocopied onto art cels.

Hundreds of talented artists draw and paint the art cels for filming the animation.

The hand-painted art cels move across the background at a rate of 24 cels per second.

Each art cel is placed on the appropriate background and photographed in the Camera Department.

The following videos from the
Animated Stories from the
New Testament are now available:
The King is Born
He is Risen
The Prodigal Son
The Good Samaritan
The Miracles of Jesus
Saul of Tarsus
The Righteous Judge
Forgive us our Debts
The Kingdom of Heaven
Who is Rich?
The Ministry of Paul

Talented composer, Lex de Azevedo, uses his musical talents to create the necessary mood for each animation.

The sound effects, voices, music, and film are mixed together in Burbank, California.